This Book Belongs To:

~~MELISSA~~

and

~~Mike~~ Marco

Madelyn

Daniel and the Lions

Once, there was a king named Darius. He had a very large kingdom, and could not be everywhere at once. King Darius decided to appoint three trusted men as governors to help him. His most trusted governor was named Daniel. He was honest and did his job well. The King put Daniel in charge of the other governors.

The other governors were very jealous of Daniel and wanted to get rid of him. They thought hard to come up with a plan that would make Daniel look bad to the King.

Daniel, however, never did anything wrong. He was honest and worked hard. Daniel prayed to God three times a day and had only good in his heart.

Since Daniel was such a good person and obeyed all the laws, the other governors would need the King to make a new law that Daniel would break. There was only one law they could think of that Daniel might not obey.

The two governors, first, went to King Darius and told him he was the greatest king that ever lived.

They said that Darius was so great,
that all people should pray *only* to
him for one whole month. If anyone
broke this new law by praying to
God, they would be thrown into a
den of hungry lions as punishment.

Darius was very flattered by this.
He thought it was a good idea, and so
he signed the law.

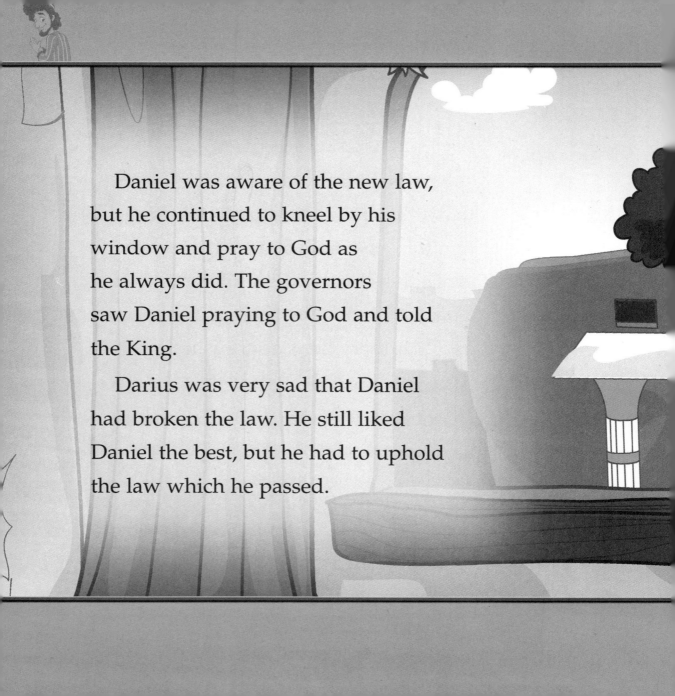

Daniel was aware of the new law, but he continued to kneel by his window and pray to God as he always did. The governors saw Daniel praying to God and told the King.

Darius was very sad that Daniel had broken the law. He still liked Daniel the best, but he had to uphold the law which he passed.

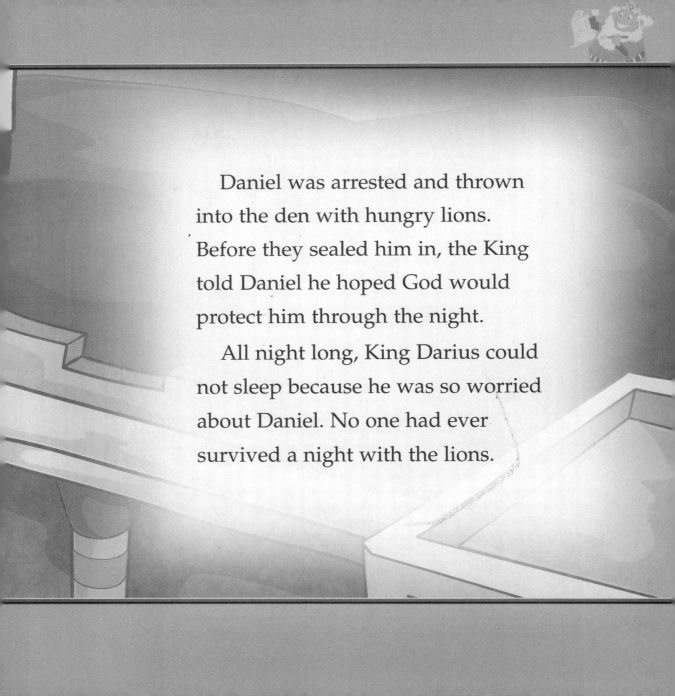

Daniel was arrested and thrown into the den with hungry lions. Before they sealed him in, the King told Daniel he hoped God would protect him through the night.

All night long, King Darius could not sleep because he was so worried about Daniel. No one had ever survived a night with the lions.

Down in the den however, Daniel was not afraid at all. He knew that God would hear his prayer, and protect him from the lions.

During the night, the lions purred and played like gentle house cats. God had sent an angel to make sure the lions did not open their jaws against Daniel.

The next morning, the King rushed to the lions' den hoping to find Daniel still alive. The stone was removed from the den entrance and he called down into the den, "Daniel, are you alright?"

Daniel smiled and called back to the King that he was alive and well. He told Darius that God had protected him.

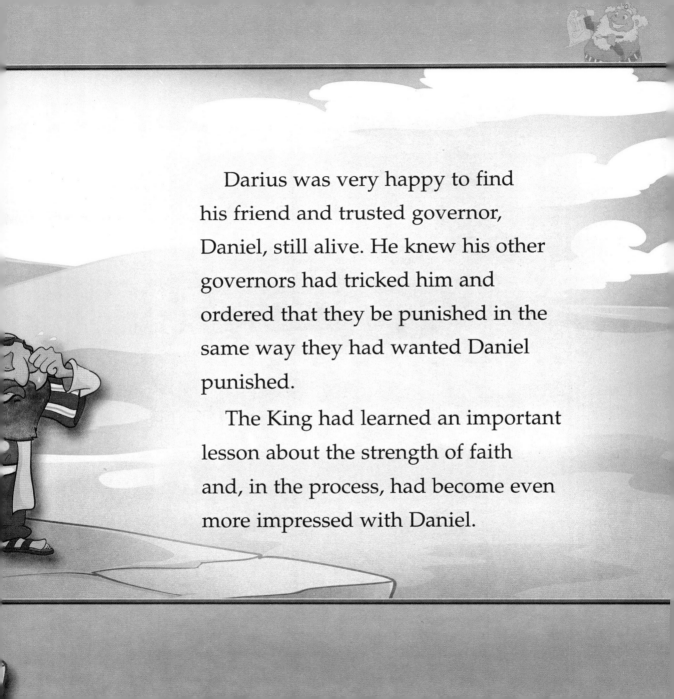

Darius was very happy to find his friend and trusted governor, Daniel, still alive. He knew his other governors had tricked him and ordered that they be punished in the same way they had wanted Daniel punished.

The King had learned an important lesson about the strength of faith and, in the process, had become even more impressed with Daniel.